Publication Rights

Disclaimer: The information in this book contains health and nutritional information and supporting data, but is not intended to replace advice from qualified practitioners.

All characters in the book are fictional and not intended to represent any particular person.

First published in 2016 by Richard Natural Enterprises.
2600 S. Finley Rd Unit 3101, Lombard, IL, 60148

A number of artists created drawings for this book, and their names or initials are at the bottom of the drawings they created.

Richard- Betty Richard
BM Brian Matuszewski
CR Chris
Laura Ross
MW- Michelle Wong
Mya-Mya Matuszewski
OE Ode

Special appreciation is expressed to Brian Matuszewski who did the layout and some of the drawings, and Betty Richard, my wife, who waited patiently at times and helped with difficult decisions.

Appreciation is expressed to the some of the main helpers who assisted with the evaluation and processing of this book: Abigail Richard, Antonella Matuszewski, Becky Hull, Erica Hall, Jessica Patella, Laura Ross, Lynn Rugaard, Marcia Egles Brown, Mary Tevis-Tuttle, Michelle Wong, Michael Arens, Nicolas Pratt, Sally Adams, Sarah Wong, Sharon Wong, and Trent Johnson.

Health food stores in the USA can obtain this book from Now Foods at 800 999 8069 item 8997. Individuals who want this book, can request their health store to order it for them.

Health stores in Canada can order this book from Pure Source at 519 837 2140, and individuals can obtain it thru their health store.

INTRODUCTION

Children love nursery rhymes and this book creates a wonderful opportunity to turn verses based on familiar nursery rhymes into learning experiences. It presents a natural health point of view and emphasizes what children can do to become healthier like "Eating your veggies". When I read traditional nursery rhymes carefully, it seems that many use old fashioned words and ideas that don't make sense or are scary to kids. My goal is to help kids be healthier and have fun at the same time.

This book is mainly for children whose parents read to them and contains a "What You Can Do" message below most verses. These messages are for the children and can be presented to them, if the reader believes this is appropriate. There are also "Interesting Information" sections by most verses which are for the adult reader, who can pass them on, if suitable.

The Appendix at the end of this book presents the research that has been published that supports the concepts in our nursery rhymes, and may help readers explain matters further.

For about ten years I served as the technical editor of the Natural Health Research Institute, a non-profit organization with the goal of improving human health by natural means. Much of the information in the Appendix is from this site (go to: www.naturalhealthresearch.org).

I am also the founder of NOW Foods, a manufacturer of health products (go to: www.nowfoods.com).

Yours in good health,

Elwood E Richard

Table of Contents

Bone Health

Humpty Dumpty sat on a chair.
Humpty Dumpty fell hard from there.
All the king's men were surprised when they found;
Humpty unbroken - he rose with a bound.
Humpty was careful and used every day;
Bone building foods to stop shell decay.

What You Can Do

Eat dairy foods. If you are allergic to calcium, enriched milk substitute can be used.
Play outdoors - the sunshine and exercise help build strong bones.
Avoid excess cola drinks - they hurt bone building.

Interesting Information

Egg shells are rich in calcium and so are bones. Egg shell powder is sometimes used as a supplement to
provide the calcium to help build strong bones. Most of the average people in the USA don't get enough calcium,
so it is wise to add calcium rich foods to your diet.

Coffee

Little Boy Blue, come beat your drum.
There's coffee out here and kids drinking some.
This leads to bad sleeping and also the jitters.
We hope that all kids could be coffee quitters.

What You Can Do

Don't start drinking coffee when you are young, it may start a habit you don't want.
Herbal teas can be used to replace hot coffee as most are caffeine free, and this is normally stated on the container when applicable.

Interesting Information

Health Canada recommends a maximum daily caffeine intake of no more than the following age-based intake limits:

4-6 years old 45 mg (slightly over 12 oz. of a typical cola drink or ¼ cup coffee)
7-9 years old 62.5 mg
10-12 years old 85 mg (about 1/2 cup of coffee or two 12 oz. cola drinks)

Cola Drinker

Diddle, Diddle Dumplin my son Nate,
Thought cola bev'rages were pretty great.
But then he learned of the acid and caffeine,
And decided to omit them from his health routine.

What You Can Do

Replace cola beverages with other soft drinks or better yet fruit & vegetable drinks.

Interesting Information

Unlike other soft drinks, cola beverages are more acidic due to the phosphoric acid content.
They also contain caffeine at the maximum level recommended for those aged 4 - 6 by Health Canada for one
12 ounce serving per day. Excess acid in the diet can be harmful to teeth, and caffeine can interfere with sleep.

Colds

Kids, please, do not sneeze
Into the open air.
Scarily, scarily, scarily, scarily
This spreads colds everywhere.

What You Can Do

Be careful not to spread germs by sneezing and avoid contact from others with colds.

Interesting Information

Colds are spread by germs which can infect those in contact with air sneezed out or by contact such as kissing, shaking hands, or touching items handled by those with colds.
Well over 200 virus strains are implicated in the cause of the common cold.
The rhinoviruses are the most common. There is no vaccine for the common cold.
The primary methods of prevention are hand washing, not touching the eyes, nose or mouth with unwashed hands, and staying away from sick people.

Dark Green Foods

I love those dark green foods,
And they're healthy too;
Just cooked or in salads;
So tasty for you.

What You Can Do

Eat good amounts when these are available.

Interesting Information

Dark green foods are a good source of Vitamin A and C and minerals like calcium.

Exercise

Jack is nimble, Jack is quick;
To run and play has done it.
It makes him strong and live more long;
Than when he first begun it.

What You Can Do

Replace TV and computer games with active games.
Try to participate in physical activities that happen on a regular basis
such as at a community recreation center.

Interesting Information

The most important aspect of lifestyle is physcial exercise.
It is probably more important than the food we eat, the air we breathe, and the water we drink.
Exercise is beneficial at all ages and improves all medical conditions (Patrick Massey, MD, PhD).

Eggs

What You Can Do

Try to get enough protein for breakfast by eating eggs if they are available.

Interesting Information

Most breakfasts are short on protein, but two eggs supply 26% of the RDA (Recommended Daily Allowence) for protein. They also supply 60% of the RDA for choline, 46% B-12, 42% for riboflavin, 28% for pantothenic acid, and about 10% or more of vitamin A, vitamin B 6, folic acid, vitamin D, iron, and zinc.

The storyteller becomes more and more exaggerated while protesting that he never was known to lie.

As I went down to Derby;
T'was on a market day.
I saw the finest eggs, sir
That ever a chicken did lay.

It's true my lads,
It's true my lads,
I never was known to lie.
If you go down to Derby
You'll see the same as I.

They had the strongest shell, sir
That ever a man did see:
They had to take a hammer
To open such eggs for me.

It's true my lads,
It's true my lads,
I never was known to lie.
If you go down to Derby
You'll see the same as I.

These eggs they had a beauty
Each with a color of gold.
And were the freshest eggs, sir
Though they were four weeks old.

It's true my lads,
It's true my lads,
I never was known to lie.
If you go down to Derby
You'll see the same as I.

These eggs were very large, sir.
Each one weighed over a pound.
It took two men to carry
Six dozen of them around.

It's true my lads,
It's true my lads,
I never was known to lie.
If you go down to Derby
You'll see the same as I.

These eggs were all organic
And full of lot's a good stuff.
Eating them made you full, sir.
Eating one was enough.

It's true my lads,
It's true my lads,
I never was known to lie.
If you go down to Derby
You'll see the same as I.

Fast Foods

What You Can Do

Try to reduce your use of fast foods that are already prepared and replace them with healthy foods that are ready to eat such as fresh fruit and vegetables, raw nuts, dried fruit, and natural snacks like popcorn.

Mary, Mary, quite contrary,
Why use those fast foods so;
With fries and pies that supersize
And greasy things all in a row?

Then said Mary, quite contrary,
"I saw their ads on TV.
I'd have no fun 'til I'd begun
The fast foods that they made for me."

But Mary, Mary, quite contrary,
They want what's in your purse.
You shouldn't buy what they supply;
Fast food will make your health worse.

And Mary, Mary, quite contrary,
Fast foods will make you sad.
For they will make a tummy ache;
You'll rue every bite that you've had.

Mary, Mary, not contrary,
Went to her health food store.
She bought the things that Nature brings
And now she has good health galore.

Interesting Information

Fast foods are those which can be purchased and consumed quickly without much time spent in preparation. Fast food use has increased in the USA and the latest information from the National Center for Health Statistics showed fast foods was just over 11% of total calories. This is true for both men and women, but older Americans use less fast food. Data from a governmental survey shows that those who eat more fast food have less healthy diets.

Eyes

Bobby Shafto has good eyes;
From eating healthy food supplies.
Veggies yellow or dark green;
Add these to your meal routine.

What You Can Do

Try to eat some yellow or dark green fruits and vegetables every day.

Interesting Information

Vitamin A is important for eye health and found in yellow and dark green fruits and vegetables.

Toothcare

Little Miss Muffet sat on a tuffet,
Brushing her teeth with care.
Said she'd been told that when she got old,
Brushing meant teeth would be there.

What You Can Do

Brush and floss your teeth regularly. Avoid sticky candy.

Interesting Information

Dental professionals recommend flossing once per day before or after brushing.
This removes particles of food stuck between teeth that adhere to dental surfaces below the gumline.

Recipe

The recipe below is intended for children that are too young to risk using stove top heat.

- Fill a large bowl with very hot water and change the water when it gets cool. Put the jar of cocoa butter in the hot water until it melts. This may take 10 minutes or more.
- Pour ½ cup of the melted cocoa butter into a small stainless bowl.
- Add 7/8 cup of non- fat dry milk with stirring to the cocoa butter.
- Also add in ¼ tsp liquid lecithin, l tbs honey, and 4 minispoons (inside the container) of Now Better Stevia Powder
- At this point you will have a thick dough which can be shaped into stars, circles, or other figures. Also dried fruit and nuts can be pressed into the dough.

The recipe can be varied using other powders to replace some of the non- fat dry milk powder, such as malted milk powder, carob powder, or cocoa powder

Healthy Candy

Granddaughters used to visit me,
To make our candy recipe.
We used various healthy food,
Depending on our candy mood.

These were ones we loved to eat,
And made not using stove top heat.
We formed it into many shapes,
And added nuts, dried fruit, or grapes.

One day they brought a neighbor friend,
Who joked about our candy blend.
She thought it sounded pretty bad,
To make health candy like we had.

But when our candy stuff was done,
She ate more than anyone.
She took our recipes and planned,
To use them for a candy stand.

Cautions:

It is best for a parent to go thru the process for the first time to be sure hands and utensils are clean and there are no problems. Depending on the age and ability of youngsters making candy, it may only take a time or two until they can do it alone. Having youngsters cooking candy on a stove top is not recommended.
Since that candy is from foods, it should be refrigerated until used, and not kept more than a week.

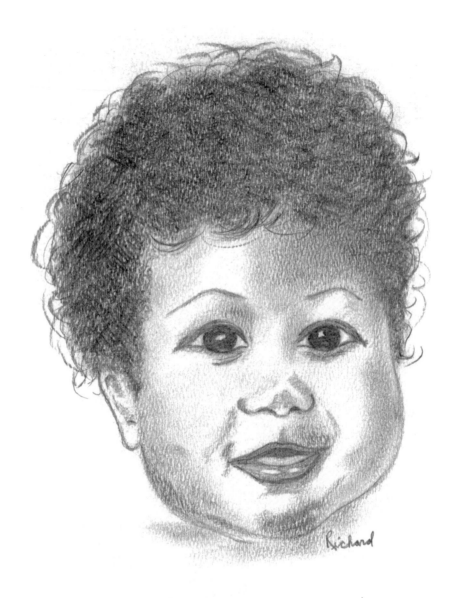

Healthy Child

All children should be healthy ones;
We hope that this can be.
And healthy habits from this book;
Can be a helpful key.

What You Can Do

Do all of the steps needed for good health. None should be left out.

Interesting Information

It takes all parts of natural health to produce a healthy child good nutrition, fresh air and water, exercise,
the right amount of sleep, and a relaxed attitude.

Healthy Lifestyle

Old King Stan was a merry old man,
And a merry old kinda guy.
He called for some treats that merry folk eats,
And also some cake and pie.

It soon was his fate that he gained excess weight,
Because of his big appetite.
He piled up his plate with the treats that he ate;
He should have been eating more right.

So his new diet plan had less pie and more bran,
And he went to the gym to be fitter.
Now just look at King Stan and follow his plan;
He's healthy; he wasn't a quitter.

What You Can Do

Don't overeat. Include salad greens and vegetables at meals and easy on the dressing. Get exercise.

Interesting Information

Two of the most important factors to consider are increasing
metabolism and controlling blood sugar. Proper diet and exercise is required to managing these important factors.
Also, no matter the diet plan, eating late can lead to weight gain. Furthermore, adding artificial sugars to your diet
may work against your weight loss goals, especially if you are not diabetic.

What You Can Do

Replace junk foods with whole grains, raw nuts, fruits, and vegetables.

Be kind to your junk food friends and share good natural food with them.
They will then see that they do better using natural foods.

Interesting Information

Junk foods are anything made principally of white flour and or refined white sugar or syrup- for example white bread, crackers, cake, candy, ice cream, soda, chocolate malts, sundaes, sweetened carbonated beverages. When junk food is consumed very often, the excess fat, carbohydrates, and processed sugar found in funk food contributes to an increased risk of cardiovascular disease, diabetes, weight gain, and many other chronic health conditions.

Junk Food Guy

Big junk food guy, each day walks by
My fruit and yogurt hut.
Says to my face, "You big disgrace,
You are a health food nut."

And when I say that's not okay,
It makes him pleased as punch.
He says it's rude to spurn good food,
Like Coke and fries for lunch.

He says "'health nut' is naughty but
Is very, very true
Your health food stuff is much too tough
Which makes it hard to chew."

He is so bad, it makes me mad
To call my food so funky.
So next day I make my reply
"You big bad fast food junky.

Your stomach noise can scare small boys.
A mess is your complexion.
Your body weight is much too great;
Your mind without direction..

I'll bet you if, you great big stiff,
You gave my food a try,
Your stomach would feel twice as good,
And be a healthy guy".

I thought the guy would never try,
My smoothies and my diet.
He said to me if it was free,
He'd be the first to try it.

Now each day we contentedly,
Eat yogurt, nuts, and fruit.
The junk food guy I gave reply,
Became a health recruit.

Pet Health

What You Can Do
If you have a pet, feed it healthy food.

Interesting Information
Most animals have similar nutritional needs to humans.
But check with your vet before giving a pet table food.

Pet Health

One of renown in our home town,
We thought was wondrous wise.
He went in for health foods galore
Where he bought health supplies.

It made you smile to see his pile,
Of powders, pills and such.
The check out guy let out a cry,
"How can you use so much?"

The wise man said with face quite red,
"You must not forget;
The stuff you see is not for me,
It's only for my pet."

I must relate, my dog looks great,
And thrives on what you see.
He goes to shows, the town all knows,
And earn awards for me.

I use a plan with kelp and bran,
To make his coat to shine.
This photo shows how my dog glows;
Are other dogs so fine?

He has a feast on brewer's yeast,
Which fills my dog with pep.
One can't believe or quite conceive
How bouncy is his step."

The counter man again began,
"Because your dog looks swell,
So likely you use health foods too,
To help your looks as well."

The wise pet guy renown'd so high,
Said, "Everybody knows
I own the pet and don't forget,
I don't compete in shows."

"I must pursue my point of view,"
Replied the counter guy.
"If it puts pep in a dog's step,
It should be worth a try."

And when he saw his reason flaw
With all his might and mane,
The man grew wise,
used health supplies,
Since now the facts were plain.

Potato on the Couch

When it comes to things athletic – he surely is no slouch,
Who changes channels fast as the potato on the couch?
When TV spot commercials come, he's in a sprinter crouch,
To get junk food supplies for the potato on the couch.

And if his couch was lumpy, he'd be slow to holler ouch,
So we must raise our praise for the potato on the couch.
If health clubs had to close their doors, this hero wouldn't grouch,
So we must hear a cheer for the potato on the couch.

He doesn't wear out tennis courts, of this we all can vouch,
And who saves park supplies like the potato on the couch.
His sacrifice has been quite nice – but caused a tummy pouch,
But who can wear it better than potato on the couch.

What You Can Do

Replace watching TV, video games, and computer games with healthful physical activities.

Interesting Information

Sedentary lifestyle From Wikipedia, Oct 15, 2016 "Increases in sedentary behaviors such as watching television are characteristic of a sedentary lifestyle. A sedentary lifestyle is a type of lifestyle with no or irregular physical activity. A person who lives a sedentary lifestyle may colloquially be known as a couch potato. …. Sedentary activities include sitting, reading, socialising, watching television, playing video games, and computer use for much of the day with little or no vigorous physical exercise. A sedentary lifestyle can contribute to many preventable causes of death.

Organic Food

This little piggy went to market.
This little piggy stayed home.
This little piggy bought junk food.
This little piggy bought none.
And this little piggy cried,
"I'll have a panic, if there's no organic,"
All the way home.

What You Can Do

Look for the organic sticker on foods you eat.

Interesting Information

The Organic Trade Association encourages consumers to avoid exposing their children to pesticides and synthetic food dyes linked to increased risk of Attention Deficit Hyperactivity. Choose organic foods when available.

Raw Nuts

Jack and Jill went up the hill
With raw nuts for a treat.
And there they found on top that mound
The taste could not be beat.

What You Can Do

Take raw nuts with you to replace junk food snacks.

Interesting Information

Research shows that people who eat nuts twice a week are 31% less likely to gain weight than those who don't eat nuts.
www.naturalhealthresearch.org

Reduce Waste

What You Can Do

Reduce the amount of trash that you create.

Interesting Information

Reused and Recycled Trash (EPA April 25, 2016). In 2013 America generated 254 million tons of trash and recycled and composed 87 million tons. From our individual waste generation of 4.40 lbs. per person per day =16,060 lbs. per person per year, a 160 lb person generates 100 times their weight per year of trash. What the people in the town in the poem should have been doing was to try to recycle and reuse materials instead of putting them into the trash.

Reduce Waste

Wee Willie Winkle went to town,
Upstairs, downstairs, in his nightgown.
He soon returned in very great haste,
Because that town was buried in waste!

They first put their waste in a big landfill,
But that got too high and began to spill.
The next place used were yards at the schools,
But these were too small and broke the state rules.

Next they put waste in their town's parks;
They were sitting there, and easy marks.
When these were full, they put trash by each street,
But soon the filling of these was complete!

So the town switched to a new way;
To ship their trash where open fields lay.
But folks living there did not agree,
And would not take their town's debris.

After this, most folks left that town.
They didn't understand what was going down.
If they had only worked to slow the trash flow,
They would not have needed to pack up and go.

We have been working with a good local organization that has developed some helpful ideas
for the area west of Chicago. You can see some of their other ideas at www.scarce.org.
Not all of these ideas can be done in your area,
but it gives you an idea of what an organization near you might be able to do.

Recycle

There was a thoughtful man with a recyling plan,
Right in the middle of the city.
The first thing that you knew most others did it too,
And everything is healthful and pretty.

What You Can Do

Help in recycling in your home, neighborhood, and school.

Interesting Information
Benefits of Recycling

Prevents pollution by reducing the need to collect new raw materials.
It saves energy.
Reduces greenhouse gas emissions that contribute to global climate change.
Helps sustain the environment for future generations.
Helps create new well-paying jobs in the recycling and manufacturing industries in the USA.

Second Hand Smoke

Second hand smoke, second hand smoke
For health it is no joke.
So when it comes
Go play with chums
"It's harmful for small folk."

What You Can Do

Avoid smoke by others. Play somewhere else. Open windows.

Interesting Information

Exposure to second hand smoke can increase risk of lower respitory pneumonia, increase prevalence of chronic middle ear disease, and aggravate the upper respiratory tract in children.

Sleep

Hey, diddle, diddle have I got a riddle,
What makes a child pretty bright?
It's waking at dawn, with a stretch and a yawn,
And getting good sleep every night.

What You Can Do

Go to bed when told by parents. Read something if you can't sleep.

Interesting Information

Americans rate sleep as more important than either diet or exercise for
staying healthy. Yet the average amount of sleep Americans get has
decreased significantly since 1998.

Spoiled Food

The King of France, he took a chance,
With spoiled food for his men.
Some had a frown when it went down,
And then came up again.

What You Can Do

Pay attention to advice from parents and teachers.

Interesting Information

Foods spoil if they sit at warm temperatures too long. Refrigeration and freezing extends the shelf life. Be careful with foods for picnics or school lunches.

Sugar

Peter, Peter, sugar eater,
Always looked for something sweeter;
Made his health and weight so bad,
He wished he'd used less than he had.

What You Can Do

Use less sugar.

Interesting Information

Consumption of these added sugars has increased the prevalence of obesity, diabetes, and dental cavities while decreasing diet quality. As a result, the Institute of Medicine now recommends a limit of 25% of total calories, the World Health Organization recommends less than 10%, and the American Heart Association recommends 5% of total calories from added sweeteners (Wikipedia).

Sugar Sweetened Drinks

Ding Dong Dop; Mary drinks sweet pop.
What made her drink, before she thought to think?
Oh, what a habit had this kid,
Who does what good sense would forbid.

What You Can Do

Replace sugar sweetened beverages with fruit or vegetable juice.

Interesting Information

Sugar sweetened drinks provide about 11% of all the calories consumed by young children.
Not all pop contains sugar, but it is considered a junk food.

Twinkies and Coke

One speaker we would often send
To grade schools so she could extend
Nutrition they could comprehend.

She used a cup to demonstrate
In hopes that they'd eliminate
The sugars in the food they ate.

With just a Twinkie and a coke
She'd demonstrate the things she spoke,
And made it clear to those small folk.

She wanted all the class to guess
The sugar content of this mess.
'Twas eighty grams, but all thought less.

She said the people living here
Will eat two thirds their weight each year,
And cause good health to disappear

One boy stood up, he wasn't slim.
He left the room; his smile was dim.
This was the same lunch given him

The little boy came back to say
He would not be at lunch that day,
He just had thrown his lunch away.

What You Can Do

Ask parents to give you fruit and nuts to take to lunch, rather than twinkies and a coke.

Interesting Information

A friend used to go to grade schools to talk about high sugar intakes in the USA. Including the corn sugar sweeteners, it is over 140 lbs. per person per year. Her demonstration was to pour level teaspoons of sugar into a clear glass cup and ask the students to raise their hands when the level in the glass reached the amount in a coke and a Twinkie. It was 22 teaspoonfuls (about 3 ounces.). All raised their hands well before she reached this amount. The little boy in the poem really did throw out his lunch.

TV

Mary had a TV set,
She loved it very well.
It helped find ways to pass the days,
But now her health's not swell.

What You Can Do

Try to replace TV watching with other activities.

Interesting Information

The Minnesota Department of Health stated "Television has been implicated in violent or aggressive behavior, substance abuse, obesity, poor body, image, decreased sleep problems and more."

Veggies

Oh, please give me veggies.
They'll do me so good
With flavors and colors
You know that you should.

These veggies so healthy
Will make me more mild.
I won't act so crazy
And won't drive you wild.

What You Can Do
Consume more vegetables.

Interesting Information

The average American diet falls short of the daily recommendation for…. Vegetables in the 2005 Dietary Guidelines for Americans….The recommended amount is 2.5 cups per day and 1.9 cups per day is the average intake. Over 92% of those aged 4-30 did not meet these recommendations.

Water

Simple Simon and his daughter,
Hiked in heat and had no water.
Made them tired and faint and dizzy,
Threw their health into a tizzy.

What You Can Do

Be sure to take water with you if none is available during exercise.

Interesting Information

Wikipedia Dec2, 2014   Some health authorities have suggested that people drink 64 oz. of water each day. In the USA the reference daily intake for total water is 168 oz. for males over 18 and 91.5 for females over 18 which includes drinking water, water in beverages, and water contained in food.

Appendix

This section is for parents and teachers to cover research on many of the subjects in the Table of Contents. Not all research is of good quality, but a section on the Natural Health Research Inst. website (NHRI) should help readers to understand it (see www.naturalhealthresearch.org/menu/Understanding Nutrition/Science/ Understanding Research) Subjects on the NHRI site are available by listing the topic desired at the search key. We use Information from Wikipedia, although it does not go thru the peer review process. When we use information from Wikipedia, it is reviewed by one of the NHRI. writers and editors.

Bone Health *(see www.naturalhealthresearch.org/menu/bone health)*
Lower rates of bone fracture are found in Asian women, who eat few if any dairy products, compared to Caucasian women who eat diets high in dairy products. The typical American diet with an emphasis on animal products, refined foods, and beverages such as soda, coffee and alcohol, is extremely acidic and requires minerals such as calcium, to be pulled from bones, to keep blood acidity in the normal range. The traditional Asian diet is richer in alkaline-forming vegetables and contains less acid-forming animal products. Most Americans are still not meeting the current national recommendations for adequate calcium intake.

Brushing and Flossing Teeth *(see ewww.wikipedia.org/flossing)*
Brushing teeth properly helps prevent cavities and … gum disease, which causes at least one-third of adult tooth loss. If teeth are not brushed correctly and frequently, it could lead to … forming tartar. Tartar hardens if not removed every 24 hours. Poor dental health has been associated with heart disease and shortened life expectancy……. most dentists recommend patients brush twice a day Most dentists recommend using a toothbrush labelled "soft", since firmer bristled toothbrushes can damage tooth enamel and irritate gums…Researchers found "some evidence from twelve studies that flossing in addition to tooth brushing reduces gingivitis compared to tooth brushing alone"

Coffee *(see wwww.naturalhealthresearch.org/menu/coffee)*
…Common symptoms include mild anxiety, jitteriness, insomnia, increased sleep latency, and reduced coordination. Caffeine can have negative effects on anxiety disorders. According to a 2011 literature review, caffeine use is positively associated with anxiety and panic disorders. At high doses, typically greater than 300mg, caffeine can both cause and worsen anxiety…. discontinuing caffeine use can significantly reduce anxiety.

Cola Beverages *(see www.naturalhealthresearch.org/menu/cola)*
The researchers attribute the adverse effects of cola consumption on bone mineral density to phosphoric acid, as it has been shown to have a (harmful) effect on bone and .. not found in other carbonated soft drinks…. Also cola beverages contain caffeine and other substances about which much less is known about possible effects on bone.

Colds *(see www.en.wikipedia.org/wiki/Common_cold)*
Colds are spread through small liquid drops. When someone with a cold sneezes or coughs, a huge number of tiny drops are sprayed through the air, and they can come to rest on objects like doorknobs, computer keyboards or railings on the subway. When you touch these objects, the viruses can spread to your hands and then easily on to your face. So avoiding touching your face with your hands is one way to lower your risk of catching a cold. Washing your hands frequently with regular soap is also a very good way of protecting yourself from colds.

Dark Green Vegetables *(see www.ars.usda/News/docs.htm?docid=23199)*
Dark leafy vegetables are a great source of nutrition. Salad greens, kale, and spinach are rich in vitamins A, C, E, and K and broccoli, bok choy, and mustard are also rich in the B vitamins. (Dark Green Vegetables) also contain high levels of fiber, iron, magnesium, potassium, and calcium.

Eggs *(see www.wikipedia.org/eggs)*
Careful storage of edible eggs is extremely important, as an improperly handled egg can contain elevated levels of sal-monella bacteria that can cause severe food poisoning. In the US, eggs are washed, and this cleans the shell. The USDA thus recommends refrigerating eggs to prevent the growth of Salmonella. Refrigeration also preserves the taste and texture. Health experts advise people to refrigerate washed eggs, use them within two weeks, cook them thoroughly, and never consume raw eggs. However, uncracked eggs can be left unrefrigerated for several months without spoiling. Chicken eggs ... supply all essential amino acids for humans ..., and provide several vitamins and minerals as signifi-cant amounts of the Daily Value, including retinol (vitamin A), riboflavin, pantothenic acid, vitamin B12, choline, and phosphorus. Some research suggests dietary cholesterol ... adversely affects the body's cholesterol profile. . However, a study published in 2010 found no link between egg consumption and type 2 diabetics.

Exercise *(see www.naturalhealthresearch.org/menu/exercise)*
The World Health Organization ... states that physical inactivity, a significant contributor to obesity, has been identified as the fourth leading risk factor for global deaths (6% of deaths globally). Physical inactivity causes 6-10% of the major non-communicable diseases in the world (heart disease, type 2 diabetes, and breast and colon cancers). In 2008, more than 5.3 million deaths could have been averted if all inactive people were active.

Eyes *(see www.naturalhealthresearch.org/menu/eyes)*
13 studies of 18,999 participants found that the following supplements decreased age-related cataracts by the follow-ing percentages: vitamin E by 25%; alpha carotene by 28%; lutein by 25%; zeaxanthin by 30%; vitamin A by 31% and vitamin C by 33%.

Fast Food *(see en.wikipedia.org/wiki/Fast_food)*
Due to their fat content, fast foods are implicated in poor health and various serious health issues such as obesity and cardiovascular diseases. Additionally, there is strong ... evidence showing that fast foods are also detrimental to appe-tite, respiratory system function, and central nervous system function.... Over the course of a year this is likely to result in a child gaining 6 extra pounds every year. A typical fast food meal in the United States includes a hamburger, French fries, and a soft drink. According to the National Institutes of Health (NIH), fast foods are quick and cheap alternatives to home-cooked meals. They are also high in saturated fat, sugar, salt and calories. Eating too much fast food has been linked to, among other things, obesity and high cholesterol.

Healthy Lifestyle *(see www.health.ri.gov/healthy weight)*
A healthy weight is one that lowers your risk of certain health conditions. Overweight and obesity are caused by eating more calories than are burned. We burn some of these calories through physical activity. When we eat more calories than we burn, the extra calories are stored as fat. The best way to reach and maintain a healthy weight is ... by consum-ing a healthy diet and being physically active. ...Being overweight or obese increases the risk of developing certain health conditions, (including), heart disease, cancer, diabetes and asthma.

Junk Food Guy *(www.en.wikipedia.org/wiki/Junk_food)*
When junk food is consumed very often, the excess fat, carbohydrate, and processed sugar found in junk food contrib-utes to an increased risk of cardiovascular disease, diabetes, weight gain, and many other chronic health conditions. Also, consumers ....are less likely to eat healthy foods like fruit, vegetables, or dairy products.

Testing on rats...suggested that junk food consumption alters brain activity in a manner similar to addictive drugs like cocaine and heroin. After many weeks with unlimited access to junk food, the pleasure centers of rat brains became desensitized, requiring more food for pleasure. After the junk food was taken away and replaced with a healthy diet, the rats starved for two weeks instead of eating a nutritious fare.

Landfills *(www.en.wikipedia.org/wiki/Landfill)*
A significant problem in landfills is that the ones close to major cities are filling up and that new ones further away are being developed. Municipal solid waste (MSW)– .... consists of everyday items people use and then throw away, such as product packaging, grass clippings, furniture, clothing, bottles, food scrap and papers. In 2010, Americans recovered almost 65 million tons of MSW (excluding composting) through recycling. From 1986 to 2009 the available landfill per person has increased by almost 30%.

RawNuts *(see www.naturalhealthresearch.org/menu/raw nuts)*
Research shows that people who eat nuts twice a week are 31% less likely to gain weight than those who don't eat nuts. Nuts provide beneficial nutrients and antioxidants for the body, which offer significant health benefits.

Organic *(see www.naturalhealthresearch.org/menu/organic)*
A new review analyzed 343 peer-reviewed publications that compared differences in the composition between organic and non-organic plant-based foods (and) found that overall, organic crops contained a 17% higher antioxidant activity level. … The study's authors note that other studies have suggested some antioxidants have been linked to a lower risk of cancer and other diseases. For further information visit www.organic-center.org

Pet Food *(Wondrous Wise) (www.en.wikipedia.org/wiki/Pet_food)*
Prepared foods and some raw ingredients may be toxic for animals, and care should be taken when feeding animals left-over food. It is known that the following foods are potentially unsafe for cats and dogs:
• Chocolate, coffee-based products and soft drinks
• Raisins and grapes
• Macadamia nuts
• Garlic (in large doses) and onions
Generally, cooked and marinated foods should be avoided, as well as sauces and gravies, which may contain ingredients that, although well tolerated by humans, may be toxic to animals. Xylitol, an alternative sweetener found in chewing gum and baked goods designed for diabetics, is highly toxic to cats, dogs and ferrets.

Reduce Waste *(see.en.wikipedia.org/wiki/Solid_waste)*
In 2013 America generated 254 million tons of trash and recycled and composed 87 million tons. (From) individual waste generation of 4.40 lbs. per person per day a 160 lb. person generates 100 times their weight per year. A significant problem in landfills is that the ones close to major cities are filling up and that new ones further away are being developed. From 1986 to 2009 the available landfill per person has increased by almost 30%.

Second Hand Smoke *(see //betobaccofree.hhs.gov/)*
Pregnant women who breathe secondhand smoke are more likely to have lower birth weight babies than women who do not breathe secondhand smoke. Once born, babies who are around cigarette smoke are more likely to:
• Get ear infections
• Develop bronchitis and pneumonia
• Die from Sudden Infant Death Syndrome (SIDS)

Secondhand smoke can cause serious health problems in children, including:
• Frequent lower respiratory illness
• Wheezing and coughing
• More frequent and severe asthma attacks
• Ear infections
For more information on secondhand smoke, visit www.betobaccofree.bbs.gov.

Sleep *(see.www.naturalhealthrsarch.org/menu/sleep)*
Compared to children who slept more than 9.4 hours per night, children sleeping less than 7.7 hours per night had 23% higher hyperactivity/impulsivity scores, a 24% higher attention-deficit/hyperactivity disorder total scores, and a 24% higher inattentive scores. These results led the researchers to conclude that "Children's short sleep duration and sleeping difficulties increase the risk for behavioral symptoms of attention-deficit/hyperactivity disorder."

Spoiled Foods *(see www.naturalhealthresearch.org/menu/spoiled foods)*
You can freeze almost any food. Some exceptions are canned food or eggs in shells. However, once the food (such as ham) is out of the can, you may freeze it. …Some foods simply don't freeze well. Examples are mayonnaise, cream sauce and lettuce. Food stored constantly at 0° F will always be safe. Only the quality suffers with lengthy freezer storage. Store all foods at 0° F or lower to retain vitamin content, color, flavor and texture. Freeze food as fast as possible to maintain its quality. Rapid freezing prevents undesirable large ice crystals from forming.
Freezer Storage Chart (0°F) Note: Freezer storage is for quality only. Frozen foods remain safe indefinitely.

Item	Months
Bacon, sausage, ham, hotdogs, and lunchmeats	1 to 2
Casseroles, gravy, meat or poultry, meat, cooked, soups and stews	2 to 3
Frozen dinners and entrees, meat, uncooked, ground, poultry, uncooked, giblets	3 to 4
Poultry, cooked	4
Meat, uncooked roasts, chops	4 to 12
Wild game, uncooked	8 to 12
Poultry, uncooked, parts	9
Egg whites or egg substitutes, poultry, uncooked, whole	12

Sugar *(see www.naturalhealthresearch.org/category/sweeteners-3/)*
A new study has suggested that elevated sugar consumption may increase cardiovascular disease even in teenagers. Compared to those in the lowest added sugar intake group (under10%), those in the highest added sugar intake group (over 30%) had 9% lower HDL levels while LDL cholesterol levels were 8% higher as well as 10% higher triglycerides. Those in the highest added sugar group also had 35% lower levels of fiber.

Sugar Sweetened Beverages *(see www.health.ri.gov/healthrisks/sugarsweetenedbeverages)*
The calories in sugar sweetened beverages can contribute to weight gain and provide little to no nutritional value. Sugar sweetened beverages do not fill you up the same way that food does. Those extra calories can lead to other health risks including obesity, tooth decay, heart disease and type 2 diabetes. There are plenty of healthy and tasty alternatives to sugar sweetened beverages...
• Choose water, or low-calorie beverages instead of sugar sweetened beverages;
• Add some freshly squeezed lemon or orange juice to plain water or sparkling water;
• Add ¼ - ½ cup of 100% juice to sparkling seltzer water;
• Make your own unsweetened iced tea with decaf tea bags or herbal tea bags;
• Use low calorie hot chocolate and low fat milk for a tasty treat;
• Make water more exciting by adding slices of lemon, lime, cucumber, or watermelon.

Television *(This is from Sept 15, 2016, but this link is no longer active www.mndnr.gov/TV dangers)*
Heavy reliance on television and other screen time has effects on the community and the individual. Minnesota …is concerned about the effects of television and other screen time on the health of individuals and the community and its role in obesity. Nearly a third of American children live in a household where the television is on all or most of the time..... the next step is to get active: go outside and take a walk, garden, play with friends or family members, walk the dog, etc. Encourage parents to keep TVs, computers, and video game consoles out of the kid's bedrooms. Children with televisions in their bedrooms have been found to watch more and eat more unhealthily

Vegetables *(see https://www.ars.usda.gov/ARSUserFiles/80400530/pdf/Pynet_94.pdf)*
The average American diet falls short of the daily recommendations for fruit and vegetables in the 2005 Dietary Guidelines for Americans... 2005 Recommendations
Food Group Dietary Guidelines recommendations for a 2000 - calorie diet

Item	Recommended Daily Servings	Used
Fruit	2 cups per day	0.9
Vegetables	2.5 cups per day	1.9
Dark green vegetables	4 cups per day	2

Whole Grains *(see www.naturalhealthresearch.org/menu/whole grains)*
American nutritional guidelines call for the consumption of at least 3 servings of wholegrains daily (but) the typical American – adult or child - consumes less than one serving … per day. Whole grains naturally contain vitamins, minerals, and other constituents that are essential for human health, most of which are removed when a grain is refined. Unrefined wholegrains naturally contain high concentrations of B vitamins: thiamine, niacin, riboflavin, and pantothenic acid, minerals (calcium, magnesium, potassium, phosphorus, sodium, and iron), essential amino acids (arginine and lysine), and vitamin E complex (tocopherols and tocotrienols).